SEPTEMBER 27, 1907: IN THE VILLAGE OF BANGA, NEAR LAHORE, THE BIRTH OF A BABY BROUGHT JOY TO THE OTHERWISE GLOOMY HOUSEHOLD OF SARDAR KISHAN SINGH.

VIDYAVATI LOOKED FONDLY AT HER BABY.
I WISH YOUR FATHER AND UNCLES WERE HERE TODAY.
VIDYAVATI'S HUSBAND, KISHAN SINGH, AND HIS TWO BROTHERS WERE THEN IN JAIL FOR OPPOSING THE BRITISH RULE IN INDIA.

SOON AFTER—
KISHAN!
MOTHER!

KISHAN SINGH AND HIS YOUNGEST BROTHER, SWARAN SINGH, COULD COME HOME BECAUSE THEY WERE RELEASED ON BAIL.
IF ONLY AJIT, TOO, WERE HERE WITH US!
AJIT SINGH, THE SECOND BROTHER WAS SERVING A SENTENCE IN THE MANDALAY JAIL IN BURMA.

JUST THEN —
A TELEGRAM, SIR.

IT'S FROM MANDALAY! AJIT HAS BEEN RELEASED!
MY GRANDSON, YOU ARE THE BHAGANWALA, THE LUCKY ONE.

KISHAN, WHEN IS AJIT COMING HOME?
WELL... NOT IMMEDIATELY, I AM AFRAID. HE HAS LEFT FOR GERMANY.

MONTHS WENT BY.
WHY DOESN'T MY SON COME HOME?
MOTHER, PLEASE TRY TO UNDERSTAND. THE MOMENT AJIT RETURNS, HE'LL BE JAILED AGAIN ON SOME PRETEXT OR OTHER.

I UNDERSTAND. BUT MY POOR DAUGHTER-IN-LAW. WHO WILL WIPE HER TEARS?

AS TIME WENT BY, AJIT SINGH'S EXILE HAD ITS IMPACT ON LITTLE BHAGAT SINGH.
MOTHER, WHY DOES AUNTIE WEEP ALL THE TIME?
SHE MISSES YOUR UNCLE.

WHY DOESN'T HE COME HOME, THEN ?
HE CAN'T, MY SON. OUR COUNTRY IS RULED BY THE BRITISH. YOUR UNCLE WANTS THEM TO LEAVE INDIA AND GO TO THEIR OWN COUNTRY.
VIDYAVATI TOLD HER SON HOW THE PEOPLE WERE STRUGGLING FOR THEIR FREEDOM.

LITTLE BHAGAT SINGH RAN TO HIS AUNT.
AUNTIE, DON'T WEEP.

WHEN I GROW UP, I'LL DRIVE THE BRITISH OUT AND BRING UNCLE HOME.

BUT THE BRITISH ARE VERY STRONG. THEY HAVE GUNS AND CANNONS.
DON'T WORRY. I TOO WILL GET GUNS.

MY BRAVE CHILD!

LATER THAT EVENING, AS KISHAN SINGH WAS STROLLING THROUGH HIS ESTATE WITH A FRIEND —
WHAT ARE YOU PLANTING, BHAGAT SINGH ?
RIFLES.

RIFLES?

WHY RIFLES?
TO FREE MY COUNTRY.

YES, BHAGAT SINGH. WE NEED RIFLES TO LIBERATE OUR LAND. AND WE NEED BRAVE BOYS LIKE YOU!

BHAGAT SINGH WAS FIRST SENT TO THE VILLAGE SCHOOL. LATER, IN 1916, HE JOINED THE D.A.V. SCHOOL AT LAHORE. HE WAS LOOKED UPON BY HIS FRIENDS AS A LEADER.
EASY ARE UTTERANCES BUT DIFFICULT IS THE SERVICE OF THE NATION. FOR THE PATH OF PATRIOTISM HAS COUNTLESS TORMENTS.

BHAGAT, WHY DO YOU ALWAYS SING THIS SONG?
BECAUSE IT USED TO BE SHAHEED KARTAR SINGH SARABHA'S FAVOURITE SONG!

BHAGAT SINGH WORSHIPPED KARTAR SINGH SARABHA WHO HAD DIED A MARTYR AT TWENTY.
HE IS MY HERO.

IN 1919, WHEN BHAGAT SINGH WAS TWELVE YEARS OLD, THE GOVERNMENT PASSED THE INFAMOUS ROWLATT ACT.
BHAGAT SINGH, WHAT IS THIS ROWLATT ACT? DO YOU KNOW?
I AM TOLD IT EMPOWERS THE GOVERNMENT TO SEND A MAN TO JAIL...

...WITHOUT A TRIAL. NO COURT, NO JUDGE. JUST PICK THE MAN UP AND LOCK HIM IN.
BHAGAT SINGH, YOU KNOW SO MUCH ABOUT THE POLICE AND JAILS!

THAT'S NOT SURPRISING. MY FATHER AND UNCLES WERE IN JAIL. THEIR CRIME? THEY LOVED OUR MOTHERLAND AS SHAHEED KARTAR SINGH DID.

UNDER THE LEADERSHIP OF GANDHIJI, PEOPLE THROUGHOUT THE COUNTRY PROTESTED AGAINST THE ROWLATT ACT WITH DEMONSTRATIONS AND MEETINGS.
VANDE MATARAM!

AT ONE SUCH MEETING HELD AT JALLIANWALLA BAGH, IN AMRITSAR —

IT WAS A MASSACRE THAT SHOCKED THE COUNTRY.
HUNDREDS OF PEOPLE HAVE BEEN KILLED AND MANY MORE INJURED.
HOW... HOW COULD GENERAL DYER FIRE AT UNARMED PEOPLE?

JALLIANWALLA BAGH! THE HOLY PLACE ANOINTED WITH THE BLOOD OF PATRIOTS! I MUST GO THERE ON A PILGRIMAGE.

BHAGAT SINGH VISITED JALLIANWALLA BAGH.
GOD! THIS WAS A DEATH-TRAP!

THE BULLETS EMBEDDED IN THESE WALLS WILL REMAIN HERE FOREVER — A MEMORIAL TO THE MARTYRS.

BHAGAT SINGH COLLECTED SOME OF THE RED EARTH.

THIS EARTH SHALL INSPIRE ME TO SACRIFICE EVERY-THING FOR THE CAUSE.

THE MASSACRE AT JALLIANWALLA BAGH STIRRED THE CONSCIENCE OF THE NATION. GANDHIJI LAUNCHED THE NON-COOPERATION MOVEMENT.
GANDHIJI HAS GIVEN A CALL TO STOP PAYING TAXES AND TO BOYCOTT SCHOOLS AND COLLEGES AIDED BY THE GOVERNMENT.
HE'S RIGHT. WE SHOULD HAVE NO TRUCK WITH THIS ALIEN GOVERNMENT.

BHAGAT SINGH JOINED THE NATIONAL COLLEGE FOUNDED BY PATRIOTIC CITIZENS. IT WAS HERE THAT HE CAME INTO CONTACT WITH SUKHDEV.
WHAT ARE YOU READING?
A BOOK ON THE HISTORY OF REVOLUTION.

DO YOU THINK WE WILL HAVE A REVOLUTION HERE IN INDIA?
YES. WHEN WE SUCCEED IN AROUSING THE PEOPLE.

HOW WILL YOU DO THAT ? OUR PEOPLE ARE ILLITERATE. AND THEY FIND LONG SPEECHES TIRESOME.
I KNOW WHAT THEY LIKE MOST — PLAYS AND MUSIC.

BHAGAT SINGH BEGAN TO ACT IN PLAYS LIKE 'RANA PRATAP' STAGED BY THE NATIONAL DRAMATIC CLUB.
DEFENDING ONE'S MOTHERLAND IS A SACRED TASK. WE'LL DO IT TO THE LAST DROP OF OUR BLOOD. NO SACRIFICE IS TOO BIG FOR FREEDOM.

THEN ONE DAY —
WHAT'S THE MATTER, BHAGAT ?
MY FATHER WANTS ME TO GET MARRIED TO PLEASE MY GRANDMOTHER. THIS IS THE SECOND LETTER FROM HIM ON THE SUBJECT.

WHAT WILL BE YOUR ANSWER ?
THAT AS LONG AS MY COUNTRY IS HELD IN SLAVERY, THE ONLY BRIDE I WILL EMBRACE IS DEATH.

BUT BHAGAT, YOUR GRAND-MOTHER WILL NOT ...
I KNOW. THAT'S WHY I HAVE DECIDED TO RUN AWAY.

BHAGAT SINGH WENT TO KANPUR AND MET GANESH SHANKAR VIDYARTHI, A GREAT PATRIOT.
SIR, I HAVE COME TO KANPUR TO ESCAPE GETTING MARRIED. I HAVE BUT ONE PASSION—TO SEE MY COUNTRY FREE!

YOUR PASSION IS LIKE THAT OF THE MOTH FOR THE FLAME. IT COULD PROVE FATAL.
I AM NOT UNAWARE OF THAT, SIR.

AND BHAGAT SINGH BEGAN TO WORK FOR VIDYARTHI'S PRATAP PRESS WHICH SPECIALISED IN NATIONALIST LITERATURE.

HE JOINED THE HINDUSTAN REPUBLIC ASSOCIATION.
WE MUST EDUCATE OUR PEOPLE ON THE NEED FOR FREEDOM.
LEAVE THAT TO US, SIR.

BHAGAT SINGH DID NOT WASTE ANY TIME. ONE DUSSERA DAY, HE AND HIS FIVE COMPANIONS ATTENDED A LOCAL FAIR AND BEGAN TO DISTRIBUTE LEAFLETS.
WAKE UP MY BROTHERS... WAKE UP... READ THIS...

SOON THEY COLLECTED A HUGE CROWD. UNFORTUNATELY, THIS ATTRACTED THE ATTENTION OF A FEW POLICEMEN IN PLAIN CLOTHES.
YOU WANT TO WAKE UP YOUR FELLOW COUNTRYMEN, DO YOU?

THEY HAVE CAUGHT TWO OF OUR FRIENDS.
DON'T WORRY.

BHAGAT SINGH FLUNG THE BUNCH OF LEAFLETS IN THE OPPOSITE DIRECTION.

WHEN THE CROWD MADE A BEE-LINE FOR THEM, HE WENT TO THE POLICEMEN.
LOOK! THOSE MISCHIEF-MONGERS ARE STILL DISTRIBUTING THE LEAFLETS.

ALMOST ALL THE POLICEMEN RUSHED TO THE OTHER SIDE TO ARREST THE 'CULPRITS'.
ONLY TWO OF THEM ARE LEFT TO GUARD OUR FRIENDS.

THE NEXT MOMENT —
WHY DON'T YOU GO AND HELP YOUR FRIENDS TO ARREST THE MISCREANTS?

AS BHAGAT SINGH AND HIS FRIENDS SPED AWAY —
WE HAVE BEEN DUPED! CHASE THEM!

WE ARE BEING CHASED.

THIS SHOULD STOP THEM.
AS ANTICIPATED, THE FRIGHTENED POLICEMEN GAVE UP THE CHASE.

BHAGAT SINGH'S STAY IN KANPUR CAME TO AN ABRUPT END. HE HAD TO LEAVE FOR LAHORE. HIS GRANDMOTHER WAS SERIOUSLY ILL.
YOU CAN GO HOME WITHOUT HESITATION. YOUR FATHER HAS SENT WORD THAT YOU WILL NOT BE ASKED TO GET MARRIED.

BHAGAT SINGH RETURNED TO LAHORE AND NURSED HIS GRANDMOTHER WITH GREAT CARE AND LOVE ...
... AND SHE SOON RECOVERED.

THOSE WERE THE DAYS WHEN THE SIKHS HAD LAUNCHED A PROTEST MOVEMENT AGAINST THE BRITISH FOR DEPOSING RIPUDAMAN SINGH, THE MAHARAJA OF NABHA.
BHAGAT, SOME SIKH JATHAS ON THEIR MARCH TO JAITO WILL BE STOPPING AT OUR VILLAGE. I WANT YOU TO LOOK AFTER THEIR COMFORTS.
I WILL LEAVE FOR BANGA IMMEDIATELY.

AT THE VILLAGE, HOWEVER —
IF WE HONOUR THE SIKH JATHAS, WE WILL BE INVITING THE WRATH OF THE GOVERNMENT.
THAT SHOULD NOT DETER US FROM OFFERING OUR HOSPITALITY TO THE GUESTS, UNCLE.

BHAGAT SINGH HAD HIS WAY. LATER —
GOD BLESS YOU, SON. YOU HAVE TAKEN GREAT PAINS TO MAKE OUR STAY COMFORTABLE.

BUT THE GOVERNMENT, AS EXPECTED, WAS ANNOYED.
YOU'D BETTER RUN, BROTHER. WARRANTS HAVE BEEN ISSUED FOR YOUR ARREST.
THANK YOU FOR THE TIP.
BHAGAT SINGH FLED TO LAHORE.

AT LAHORE, BHAGAT SINGH AND HIS FRIENDS FORMED AN ASSOCIATION CALLED "NAV JAWAN BHARAT SABHA".
I PROMISE TO PLACE THE INTERESTS OF MY COUNTRY ABOVE THOSE OF MY COMMUNITY...
NAV JAWAN BHARAT SABHA
THE SABHA WORKED FOR PATRIOTIC CAUSES LIKE THE SWADESHI MOVEMENT.

THE SABHA OBSERVED MARTYRS' DAY IN MEMORY OF RAMPRASAD BISMIL, ASHFAQULLAH KHAN AND OTHER REVOLUTIONARIES WHO HAD BEEN HANGED BY THE GOVERNMENT.
BISMILJI AND ASHFAQULLAH DIED AT THE GALLOWS, SMILING. OUR HOMAGE TO THEM CAN ONLY BE IN CARRYING ON THEIR FIGHT FOR FREEDOM.

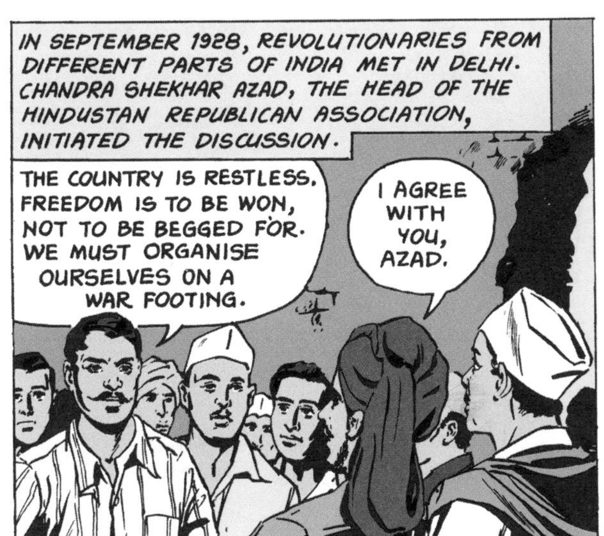
IN SEPTEMBER 1928, REVOLUTIONARIES FROM DIFFERENT PARTS OF INDIA MET IN DELHI. CHANDRA SHEKHAR AZAD, THE HEAD OF THE HINDUSTAN REPUBLICAN ASSOCIATION, INITIATED THE DISCUSSION.
THE COUNTRY IS RESTLESS. FREEDOM IS TO BE WON, NOT TO BE BEGGED FOR. WE MUST ORGANISE OURSELVES ON A WAR FOOTING.
I AGREE WITH YOU, AZAD.

AT THE CONCLUSION OF THE MEETING —
NOW LET'S DISPERSE. WE MUST BE CAREFUL. THE POLICE KNOW THAT WE ARE MEETING IN DELHI ALTHOUGH THEY DON'T KNOW EXACTLY WHERE.

THEN, DRESSED AS A POLICE CONSTABLE, BHAGAT SINGH LEFT FOR LAHORE. AT THE DELHI RAILWAY STATION A POLICE OFFICIAL ENTERED HIS COMPARTMENT.
WHAT IS YOUR NAME? WHICH POLICE STATION ARE YOU ATTACHED TO AND WHY ARE YOU HERE?
SIR, I AM KARTAR SINGH FROM NIHAL SINGH WALA POLICE STATION. I ESCORTED SOME PRISONERS TO DELHI.

SHOW ME YOUR RAILWAY PASS.
MY COLLEAGUE HAS GONE TO GET IT ENDORSED.

I SEE.
I DON'T THINK HE BELIEVES ME.

THE POLICE OFFICIAL LEFT THE COMPARTMENT.
HE'S SURE TO CHECK WITH THE BOOKING OFFICE.

BHAGAT SINGH ENTERED ANOTHER COMPARTMENT AND LOCKED HIMSELF UP IN THE LAVATORY. AS THE TRAIN BEGAN TO LEAVE THE STATION, THE POLICE OFFICIAL RETURNED WITH A FEW CONSTABLES...
...AND BOARDED IT.

THE ROGUE MUST BE SOMEWHERE HERE. MAKE A THOROUGH SEARCH.

WHEN THE TRAIN REACHED THE NEXT STATION —
WE HAVE LOOKED EVERYWHERE, SIR. WE CAN'T FIND HIM.

LITTLE DID THEY REALISE THAT THE MAN THEY WERE LOOKING FOR WAS SEATED RIGHT THERE WITH A COPY OF THE GITA IN HIS HAND.

ON HIS RETURN TO LAHORE, BHAGAT SINGH CALLED A MEETING OF THE NAV JAWAN BHARAT SABHA.
WHAT SHOULD BE OUR STAND ON THE SIMON COMMISSION?
IT DOES NOT HAVE A SINGLE INDIAN MEMBER ON IT!
THE SIMON COMMISSION WAS APPOINTED BY THE BRITISH TO STUDY THE POLITICAL SITUATION IN THE COUNTRY.

WE MUST JOIN THE ALL-PARTIES PROCESSION AGAINST THE VISIT OF THE SIMON COMMISSION.

ON OCTOBER 30, 1928, A HUGE PROCESSION WAS TAKEN OUT BY LALA LAJPAT RAI, THE GREAT LEADER FROM THE PUNJAB.
GO BACK! SIMON COMMISSION GO BACK!
SIMON GO BACK
INDIA FOR INDIANS.

A POLICE PARTY STOPPED THE PROCESSION NEAR THE RAILWAY STATION.
TURN BACK AND DISPERSE.

BUT LALAJI MARCHED AHEAD. THEN THE POLICE RESORTED TO A LATHI CHARGE.
IT IS BARBAROUS TO ATTACK UNARMED, AND NON-VIOLENT PEOPLE.

ONE LATHI CAME DOWN ON THE UMBRELLA WHICH LALAJI WAS HOLDING.
NO!

BHAGAT SINGH AND HIS COMRADES THREW A CORDON ROUND LALAJI. YET HE WAS HIT ON HIS SHOULDER AND CHEST.

LATER IN THE EVENING —
DO YOU KNOW WHAT LALAJI SAID?
YES, I DO. THE LION OF THE PUNJAB ROARED: I DECLARE THAT EVERY BLOW THEY HURLED AT US DROVE ONE MORE NAIL INTO THE COFFIN OF THE EMPIRE.

LALAJI NEVER RECOVERED FROM THE BLOWS HE RECEIVED. HE DIED TWO WEEKS LATER.
LALAJI'S NON-VIOLENCE WAS REWARDED WITH FATAL BLOWS.
THIS GOVERNMENT UNDERSTANDS ONLY ONE LANGUAGE — BLOOD FOR BLOOD.

CHANDRA SHEKHAR AZAD NOW ARRIVED IN LAHORE TO DISCUSS PLANS FOR REVENGE.
FRIENDS, WE ARE FIGHTING A WAR OF INDEPENDENCE. THE BRITISH HAVE SOLDIERS, WEAPONS AND UNLIMITED RESOURCES. WE HAVE ONLY THE SPIRIT OF SACRIFICE.

TO AVENGE THE DEATH OF ONE INDIAN, TEN ENGLISHMEN MUST DIE. AND SINCE SCOTT, THE SUPERINTENDENT OF POLICE RAISED HIS LATHI AGAINST LALAJI, HE SHALL DIE FIRST.

ON DECEMBER 17, 1928, BHAGAT SINGH AND HIS COMRADE, RAJGURU TOOK THEIR POSITIONS NEAR THE POLICE STATION.
JAIGOPAL WILL SIGNAL TO US AS SOON AS SCOTT COMES OUT.
POLICE STATION
D.A.V. COL

JAIGOPAL WHO HAD STATIONED HIMSELF JUST OPPOSITE THE POLICE STATION WAS PRETENDING TO REPAIR HIS BICYCLE.
LOOK! THAT OFFICER IS WALKING TOWARDS THE MOTOR-CYCLE. IS HE SCOTT?

YES, HE IS OUR MAN. JAI GOPAL HAS SIGNALLED.
TAKE AIM, THEN.

EVEN AS THE WHITE MAN WAS STARTING THE MOTOR-CYCLE, HE WAS HIT BY A VOLLEY OF BULLETS.

AS BHAGAT SINGH AND RAJGURU RAN TOWARDS THE D.A.V. COLLEGE JUST OPPOSITE THE POLICE STATION, THEY WERE CHASED BY A POLICE CONSTABLE.
KEEP RUNNING. AZAD AND SUKHDEV WILL TAKE CARE OF HIM.

AZAD DID NOT FAIL THEM. HE WAS READY.
ONE STEP FORWARD AND I'LL SHOOT. GO BACK!

THE CONSTABLE IGNORED THE WARNING AND PAID FOR IT WITH HIS LIFE.

MEANWHILE, BHAGAT SINGH AND RAJGURU HAD REACHED THE QUADRANGLE OF THE COLLEGE.

THEY WENT UP TO THE FIRST FLOOR...

...ENTERED A ROOM...

...SCRAMBLED OUT OF THE WINDOW...

...SLITHERED DOWN A WATER-PIPE AND...

...MOUNTING THE BICYCLE LEFT THERE FOR THEM...

... GOT AWAY.

LATER, THEY REALISED THAT THE MAN THEY HAD KILLED WAS SAUNDERS, THE ASSISTANT SUPERINTENDENT OF POLICE AND NOT SCOTT.
NEVER MIND. HE IS ALSO A WHITE POLICE OFFICIAL, A BRITISH IMPERIALIST.
WE MUST MAKE THAT CLEAR TO THE PEOPLE.

ON THE FOLLOWING DAY, NOTICES APPEARED ALL OVER THE CITY.
HINDUSTAN SOCIALIST REPUBLICAN ASSOCIATION
WE REGRET THAT A WHITE MAN HAD TO BE KILLED, BUT HE WAS PART AND PARCEL OF THE INHUMAN, UNJUST BRITISH RULE WHICH HAS TO BE DESTROYED...

THE WHOLE OF THE PUNJAB RESOUNDED WITH THE NEWS.
LALAJI'S MURDER HAS BEEN AVENGED!
WHOEVER IS RESPONSIBLE FOR IT, HAS ERASED THE STIGMA OF NATIONAL INSULT.

MEANWHILE, POLICE GUARDS KEPT WATCH OVER ALL ROADS LEADING OUT OF LAHORE...

...AS WELL AS AT THE RAILWAY STATION.
WATCH OUT FOR THE CRIMINALS! ONE OF THEM IS A YOUNG SIKH.
YES, SIR.

AS THE ATTENTION OF THE POLICE WAS FOCUSSED ON THOSE WHO WERE TRAVELLING ALONE, THEY HARDLY NOTICED THE TONGA WHICH BROUGHT A PROSPEROUS LOOKING FAMILY TO THE STATION.

THE ELEGANTLY DRESSED SAHIB WALKED UP TO THE BOOKING OFFICE WINDOW. HIS WIFE AND CHILD AND A SERVANT FOLLOWED.

THE SAHIB BOUGHT THE TICKETS AND THE POLICE LET THE PARTY ENTER THE PLATFORM.

THE SAHIB AND HIS WIFE BOARDED A FIRST CLASS COMPARTMENT, AND THE SERVANT, A THIRD CLASS COMPARTMENT.

THE BIRDS HAD FLOWN! THE SAHIB WAS NONE OTHER THAN BHAGAT SINGH WHO HAD SHAVED OFF HIS BEARD TO AVOID DETECTION; THE WOMAN WHO POSED AS HIS WIFE WAS DURGA BHABHI, THE WIFE OF A REVOLUTIONARY, BHAGWATI CHARAN; AND THE MAN WHO ACCOMPANIED THEM AS THEIR SERVANT WAS RAJGURU!

CHANDRASHEKHAR AZAD GOT AWAY TO MATHURA, POSING AS A SADHU.

BHAGAT SINGH MEANWHILE HAD TRAVELLED EASTWARDS TO CALCUTTA. THERE HE MET JATIN DAS, A REVOLUTIONARY.
JATIN, TEACH ME HOW TO MAKE BOMBS. WE NEED THEM.
I WILL GLADLY HELP YOU.

LATER, A BOMB MANUFACTURING CENTRE WAS OPENED IN AGRA. AT A MEETING HELD THERE, THE REVOLUTIONARIES DISCUSSED THEIR FUTURE COURSE OF ACTION.
THE GOVERNMENT IS BENT ON GETTING THE TRADE DISPUTE BILL AND THE PUBLIC SAFETY BILL PASSED.

THESE BILLS WERE MEANT TO SUPPRESS THE LABOUR CLASS AND EMPOWERED THE GOVERNMENT TO JAIL ANYONE WITHOUT GIVING A REASON.
THE BRITISH WANT TO CRUSH US... THE EYES OF BRITISH AND INDIAN MEMBERS OF THE ASSEMBLY WILL HAVE TO BE OPENED.
BUT HOW?

THE DAY THE BILL IS INTRODUCED, BOMBS SHOULD BE THROWN. WE WILL MAKE A NOISE LOUD ENOUGH TO BE HEARD BY THE DEAF.

A GOOD IDEA! BUT MAKE SURE THAT THE BOMB HURTS NOBODY. WE MUST MAKE PLANS TO ENTER THE ASSEMBLY, THROW THE BOMB AND ESCAPE...
NO!

THE ONE WHO THROWS THE BOMB SHOULD COURT ARREST. LATER HE SHOULD USE THE COURT AS A PLATFORM TO EXPRESS OUR IDEOLOGY... TO ROUSE PUBLIC OPINION. OUR ARREST AND SUBSEQUENT TRIAL WILL ACT AS A DAILY REMINDER TO THE PEOPLE OF THE OBJECTIVES THEY HAVE BEFORE THEM.

SO ON APRIL 8, 1929 WHEN THE CENTRAL ASSEMBLY MET TO DISCUSS THE BILLS, BHAGAT SINGH AND HIS COMPANION, BATUKESHWAR DUTT, STOOD UP IN THE VISITORS' GALLERY.

INQUILAB ZINDABAD!

THE BOMB WAS THROWN. IT HURT NOBODY. SOME LEAFLETS TOO WERE THROWN.

THE TWO REVOLUTIONARIES CONTINUED TO SHOUT SLOGANS TILL THE POLICE CAME FOR THEM. THEY DID NOT RESIST ARREST.
YOU ARE UNDER ARREST.
DON'T WORRY. WE SHALL TELL THE WHOLE WORLD WE DID IT.

BHAGAT SINGH AND DUTT WERE TAKEN TO THE POLICE STATION. ON THE WAY THEY PASSED THE TONGA CARRYING DURGA BHABHI, HER HUSBAND AND THEIR LITTLE SON.
LAMME CHACHA!*

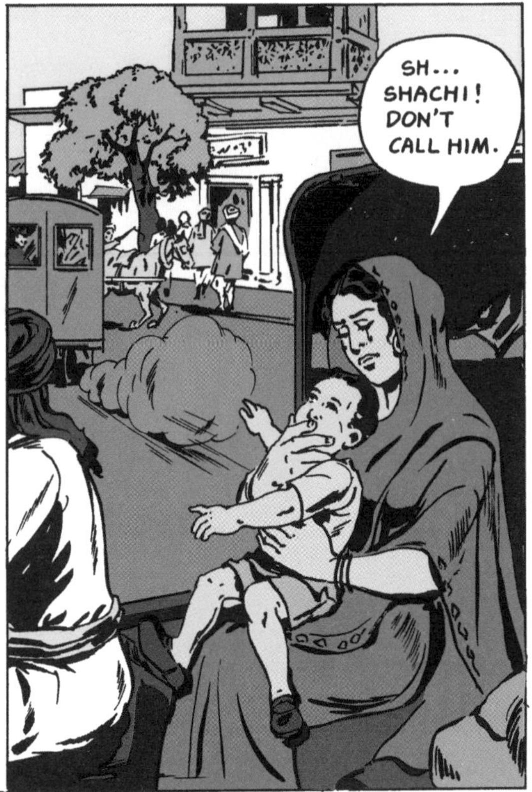
SH... SHACHI! DON'T CALL HIM.

LATER IN THE MAGISTRATE'S COURT, ASAF ALI, THE LAWYER, READ OUT THE STATEMENT PREPARED BY BHAGAT SINGH.
WE DROPPED THE BOMB ...TO REGISTER OUR PROTEST ON BEHALF OF THOSE WHO HAD NO OTHER MEANS LEFT TO GIVE EXPRESSION TO THEIR HEART-RENDING AGONY...

...OUR SOLE PURPOSE WAS TO MAKE THE DEAF HEAR AND GIVE THE HEEDLESS A TIMELY WARNING.

THE TWO REVOLUTIONARIES WERE SENTENCED TO TRANSPORTATION FOR LIFE. THEY FILED AN APPEAL IN THE HIGH COURT.
GENERAL DYER KILLED HUNDREDS OF PERSONS IN JALLIANWALLA BAGH. HE WAS GIVEN LAKHS OF RUPEES AS A REWARD BY HIS COUNTRYMEN.

IN CONTRAST, WE THROW A WEAK BOMB ENSURING THAT NO ONE IS HURT. WE ARE TRIED AND GIVEN A LIFE SENTENCE.

OUR MOTIVE WAS NOT TO KILL, BUT TO MAKE OUR IDEALS HEARD AND ACCEPTED.
AS EXPECTED, THE HIGH COURT UPHELD THE JUDGEMENT OF THE SESSIONS COURT.

LATER BHAGAT SINGH WAS SHIFTED TO THE LAHORE CENTRAL JAIL.
I WOULD LIKE TO HAVE SOME BOOKS...
BOOKS? DO YOU THINK THIS IS A LIBRARY?

THAT NIGHT —
WHAT IS THIS? THIS FOOD IS UNFIT FOR HUMAN CONSUMPTION.
YOU ARE A CRIMINAL. BE GRATEFUL FOR WHAT YOU ARE GIVEN.

BHAGAT SINGH WAS SHOCKED AT THE TREATMENT METED OUT TO POLITICAL PRISONERS.
FRIENDS, OUTSIDE THE JAIL WE FIGHT FOR FREEDOM. INSIDE THE JAIL WE MUST FIGHT FOR OUR HONOUR.

WE ARE PRISONERS BUT OUR HUMAN DIGNITY MUST BE RESPECTED. LET US GO ON A HUNGER STRIKE IN PROTEST.
WE ARE WITH YOU.
THE GOVERNMENT DID RESPOND BUT NOT BEFORE JATIN DAS, ONE OF THOSE ON A HUNGER STRIKE, DIED A MARTYR.

MEANWHILE THE GOVERNMENT HAD CAST ITS NET FAR AND WIDE. SEVERAL REVOLUTIONARIES HAD BEEN ARRESTED. BHAGAT SINGH AND HIS COMRADES, RAJGURU AND SUKHDEV WERE TRIED FOR SAUNDERS' MURDER. KISHAN SINGH CAME RUSHING TO THE JAIL.
MY SON, I WILL GET THE BEST LAWYER AVAILABLE TO DEFEND YOU AND SECURE YOUR RELEASE.
NO, FATHER. THE GOVERNMENT, ITS LAW COURTS AND VERDICTS MEAN NOTHING TO ME.

KISHAN SINGH LEFT THE JAIL WITH A HEAVY HEART.
MY SON DOESN'T KNOW WHAT IS GOOD FOR HIM. I WILL SUBMIT A PETITION TO THE GOVERN-MENT...

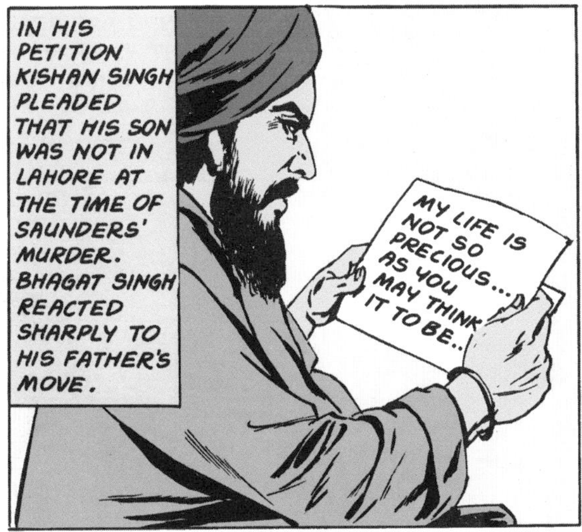
IN HIS PETITION KISHAN SINGH PLEADED THAT HIS SON WAS NOT IN LAHORE AT THE TIME OF SAUNDERS' MURDER. BHAGAT SINGH REACTED SHARPLY TO HIS FATHER'S MOVE.
MY LIFE IS NOT SO PRECIOUS... AS YOU MAY THINK IT TO BE..

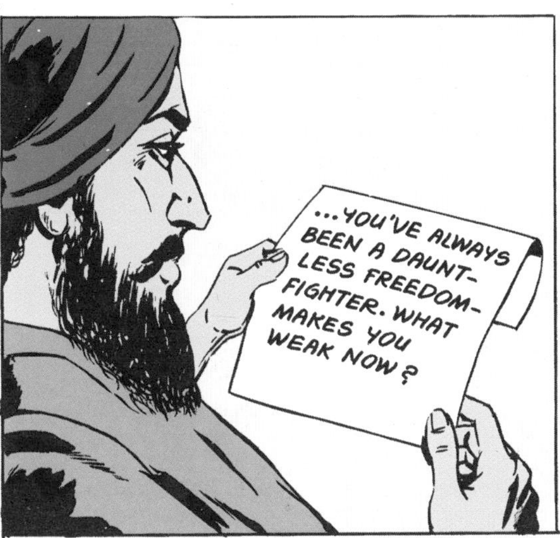
...YOU'VE ALWAYS BEEN A DAUNT-LESS FREEDOM-FIGHTER. WHAT MAKES YOU WEAK NOW?

MY SON, FORGIVE ME!

ON OCTOBER 7, 1930, THE STATE ADVOCATE CALLED ON BHAGAT SINGH.
SARDAR, I'M SORRY. THE COURT HAS AWARDED YOU THE DEATH SENTENCE.
YES. SO I'VE HEARD. BUT NO ONE NEED FEEL SORRY FOR ME.

YOU ARE BRAVE. BUT TO DIE AT THIS YOUNG AGE...! I ADVISE YOU TO SUBMIT A MERCY PETITION.
THERE IS NO NEED.

WHY NOT?
IT IS BETTER TO DIE BRAVELY THAN TO CRINGE BEFORE THE ENEMY.

I AM THE MOTH OF THE FLAME OF LIBERTY.

BHAGAT SINGH'S MOTHER, VIDYAVATI, WAS EQUALLY BRAVE. WHEN SHE MET HER SON IN JAIL —
SON, DEATH CLAIMS EVERYONE. YET DYING FOR A NOBLE CAUSE IS THE PRIVILEGE GIVEN TO A CHOSEN FEW. I AM PROUD OF YOU.

BUT HIS YOUNGEST BROTHER, KULTAR SINGH, COULD NOT WITHHOLD HIS TEARS. LATER, BHAGAT SINGH WROTE HIM A LETTER.
IT PAINED ME TO SEE TEARS IN YOUR EYES TODAY... DON'T LOSE HEART... WHAT MORE CAN I WRITE?

BHAGAT SINGH WAS TO BE HANGED ON MARCH 23, 1931. WHEN THE JAILOR WENT TO HIS CELL, BHAGAT SINGH WAS READING A BOOK ON THE LIFE OF LENIN, THE GREAT RUSSIAN REVOLUTIONARY.
SARDAR, WE HAVE COME TO LEAD YOU TO THE GALLOWS.

JUST A MOMENT PLEASE. LET ONE REVOLUTIONARY MEET ANOTHER.

A FEW SECONDS LATER, HE CLOSED THE BOOK AND GOT UP.

SUKHDEV AND RAJGURU WERE BROUGHT FROM THEIR CELLS. AT 7·00 P.M. THE LAST JOURNEY BEGAN. BHAGAT SINGH BURST INTO SONG.
YOU WILL KILL US BUT NOT THE PATRIOTISM IN US. THE FRAGRANCE OF FREEDOM SHALL RISE FROM OUR PYRES.

HEARING THE SONG, OTHER PRISONERS IN THE JAIL RAISED PATRIOTIC CRIES.
INQUILAB ZINDABAD!
UP WITH THE NATIONAL FLAG.

THE THREE REVOLUTIONARIES MARCHED UP TO THE GALLOWS, WATCHED BY THE OFFICIALS. THEN BHAGAT SINGH TURNED TO THE BRITISH DEPUTY COMMISSIONER.
WELL, MR. MAGISTRATE, YOU ARE LUCKY. TODAY YOU SHALL SEE HOW INDIANS EMBRACE DEATH WITH PLEASURE FOR THE SAKE OF THEIR SUPREME IDEAL.

THEN THE LAHORE JAIL RESOUNDED WITH A POWERFUL CRY—
INQUILAB ZINDABAD!

THE VOICE WAS STILLED FOR A MOMENT WHEN THE HANGMAN PULLED THE ROPE. BUT THE CRY WAS TAKEN UP BY MILLIONS OF INDIANS.
INQUILAB ZINDABAD!
INQUILAB ZINDABAD

"THE LESSON WHICH WE SHOULD LEARN FROM BHAGAT SINGH IS TO DIE IN A MANLY AND BOLD MANNER SO THAT INDIA MIGHT LIVE," WROTE JAWAHARLAL NEHRU OF THIS VALIANT YOUNG MARTYR.

SUBSCRIBE NOW!

Additional 10% OFF on purchase from www.amarchitrakatha.com
Coupon Code: ACKTINKLE10

TINKLE COMBO MAGAZINE + DIGEST
1 year subscription

Pay only
₹1200
₹880!
TINKLE
TINKLE DIGEST
TINKLE

FREE
2 Time Compass DVDs worth ₹598

TINKLE MAGAZINE
1 year subscription

Pay only
₹480
₹380!
TINKLE

I would like a one year subscription for
TINKLE COMBO ☐ **TINKLE MAGAZINE** ☐
(Please tick the appropriate box)

YOUR DETAILS*

Name: .... Date of Birth: |__|__| / |__|__| / |__|__|__|__|

Address: ....

.... City: .... Pin: |__|__|__|__|__|__| State: ....

School: .... Class: ....

Tel: .... Mobile: + 91 - |__|__|__|__|__|__|__|__|__|__|

Email: .... Signature: ....

PAYMENT OPTIONS

☐ Cheque /DD:

Please find enclosed Cheque /DD no. |__|__|__|__|__|__| drawn in favour of 'ACK Media Direct Pvt. Ltd.'

at .... (bank) for the amount ....,

dated |__|__| / |__|__| / |__|__|__|__| and send it to: IBH Books & Magazines Distributers Pvt. Ltd., Arch No. 30, West Approach, Below Mahalaxmi Bridge, Mahalaxmi (W), Mumbai - 400034.

☐ Pay Cash on Delivery: Pay cash on delivery of the first issue to the postman. (Additional charge of ₹50 applicable)

☐ Pay by money order: Pay by money order in favour of "ACK Media Direct Pvt. Ltd."

☐ Online subscription: Please visit: www.amarchitrakatha.com

For any queries or further information: Email: customerservice@ack-media.com or Call: 022-40497435 / 36